Dear Baby

Messages of love from friends and family

LTP
London

How to use this book

The arrival of a new baby is a wonderful occasion.
Friends and family come to celebrate, and to share their
thoughts and feelings on that first special meeting.

This beautiful gift book is the perfect place to record these hopes,
dreams and messages of love, creating a treasured keepsake
that will last forever.

*Welcome to the world,
little one!*

This book is for...

Name ....

Born on ....

Welcome to the world

The place you were born:

The time:

Your *hair* was:

Your *eyes* were:

You looked like:

Your *weight* was:

Your *length* was:

Who was there:

Dear Baby...

with *love* from

. . . .

date

. . . .

"A baby will make love stronger,
days shorter, nights longer, bankroll smaller, home
happier, clothes shabbier, the past forgotten,
and the future worth living for."

Anonymous

Dear Baby...

with love from .... date ....

Dear Baby...

I think you look *just like*:

The *cutest* thing about you is:

When I first met you, you were wearing:

with *love* from

....

date

....

Dear Baby...

with *love* from

....
date

....

Dear Baby...

My dream for you:

How I know your family:

What happened when I met you:

with love from

....

date

....

Dear Baby...

with *love* from

....

date

....

Dear Baby...

Never be afraid to:

I'll give the best *advice* about:

When you grow up,
I think you'll:

with *love* from

....

date

....

Dear Baby...

with *love* from

....

date

....

Dear Baby...

with *love* from ....

date ....

"A child's life is like a piece of paper on which every person leaves a mark."

Chinese Proverb

Dear Baby...

with *love* from

....

date

....

Dear Baby...

When I first met you, you were wearing:

The cutest thing about you is:

I think you look just like:

with love from

....

date

....

Dear Baby...

with *love* from

. . . .

date

. . . .

Dear Baby...

What happened
when I met you:

My *dream* for you:

How I know your *family*:

with *love* from

....

date ....

Dear Baby...

with *love* from ....

date ....

Dear Baby...

When you grow up,
I think you'll:

I'll give the best
advice about:

Never be afraid to:

with **love** from

....
date

....

Dear Baby...

with *love* from

....

date

....

Dear Baby...

with *love* from

· · · · · · · · · · · · · · · · · ·

date

· · · · · · · · · · · · · · · · · ·

Dear Baby...

with love from .... date ....

"Every baby born into
this world is a finer one than the last."

Charles Dickens

Dear Baby...

When I first met you,
you were wearing:

The **cutest**
thing about you is:

I think you look *just like*:

with **love** from

....

date

....

Dear Baby...

with *love* from

....

date

....

Dear Baby...

What happened when I met you:

My *dream* for you:

How I know your *family*:

with *love* from

....

date ....

Dear Baby...

with *love* from ....

date ....

Dear Baby...

When you grow up,
I think you'll:

Never be afraid to:

I'll give the best
advice about:

with love from

....

date ....

Dear Baby...

with *love* from

....

date

....

"Let her sleep, for when she wakes,
she will move mountains."

Napoleon

Dear Baby...

with *love* from

....

date

....

Dear Baby...

with *love* from

....

date

....

Dear Baby...

When I first met you, you were wearing:

I think you look *just like*:

The *cutest* thing about you is:

with *love* from

....

date

....

Dear Baby...

with love from

....

date

....

Dear Baby...

My dream for you:

What happened
when I met you:

How I know your family:

with love from

. . . .

date

. . . .

Dear Baby...

with *love* from

....

date

....

Dear Baby...

When you grow up,
I think you'll:

Never be afraid to:

I'll give the best
advice about:

with *love* from

....

date

....

Dear Baby...

with *love* from

. . . .

date

. . . .

Dear Baby...

with *love* from .... date ....

"Dreams do come true, if only
we wish hard enough."

J. M. Barrie

Dear Baby...

with *love* from

· · · · · · · · · · · · ·

date

· · · · · · · · · · · · ·

LTP
1 The Coda Centre, 189 Munster Road, London SW6 6AW
www.littletiger.co.uk

First published in Great Britain 2017

A CIP catalogue record for this book is available from the British Library

Printed in China • LTP/2700/1666/1116

2 4 6 8 10 9 7 5 3 1